HANDY IDEAS FOR HASSLED HISTORY TEACHERS

Alan Siddall, Keith Geary, Malcolm Woodcock.

Collins Educational

© CollinsEducational 1991
An imprint of HarperCollins*Publishers*
77-85 Fulham Palace Road
Hammersmith
London W6 8JB

Reprinted 1992

ISBN 0 00 329476 5

Any educational institution that has purchased one copy of this publication may make duplicate copies for use exclusively within that institution.
Permission does not extend to reproduction, storage in a retrieval system or transmittal, in any form or by any means, electronic, mechanical, photocopying, recording or otherwise, of duplicate copies for loaning, renting or selling to any other institution without the prior consent in writing of the publisher.

Hand lettering by Carol Kemp
Artwork by Michael McGrath
Cover artwork by Elaine Baker
Printed by Holmes McDougall Ltd., Edinburgh

Contents

	Teachers' notes	v
1	All my own work — *diaries*	1
2	Pass it on — *oral history*	2
3	At our mother's knee — *nursery rhymes*	3
4	Meet the family — *family trees*	4
5	Time — *chronology*	5
6	Time capsule — *evidence*	6
7	Names, names and more names — *personal names*	7
8	What's in a name? — *placenames*	8
9	Streetwise — *streetnames*	10
10	Finding food, stone-age style — *hunter/gatherers*	11
11	Burial — *ancient burial customs*	12
12	The secret of the pharaohs — *hieroglyphics*	13
13	Month by month — *Roman calendar*	14
14	The mean machine — *a Roman soldier*	15
15	Hadrian's wall — *Roman army*	16
16	Count with the Romans — *Roman numbers*	17
17	Sail away — *Viking ships*	18
18	Viking traders	19
19	Castles — *site and situation*	20
20	Attack! — *medieval warfare*	21
21	I'll scratch your back — *feudal system*	22
22	Domesday — *Domesday book*	23
23	The three field trick — *medieval farming*	24
24	The men from the Guildhall — *medieval guilds*	25
25	Fair cop gov — *medieval justice*	26
26	The pilgrim: medieval tourist — *pilgrimages*	27
27	Identify yourself — *heraldry*	28
28	Look in the church — *medieval saints*	30
29	That's entertainment	31
30	Have you met the wife? — *Henry VIII and wives*	32
31	Remember, remember — *Guy Fawkes*	33

32	Ring o' ring o' roses — *plague*	34
33	A little knowledge is a dangerous thing — *witchcraft*	35
34	How my lord and lady dress — *18th century dress*	36
35	Roll on — *18th century transport*	37
36	Highway — *travel game: roads in the 18th century*	38
37	Down on the farm — *agricultural revolution*	39
38	Black gold — *coal mining*	40
	Outline map of the British Isles	41
	Outline map of Europe	42

Teachers' Notes

These worksheets are designed to be free-standing. They are not meant to form a complete scheme of work, but are rather to be seen as back-up and additional resource material ideally suited to homework. It is our intention that they should be fun to do, as well as being worthwhile historical exercises. There are opportunities for written work, map work, colouring (the sheets themselves may be coloured in), follow-up work and research activities. Many of the sheets may provide ideas and starting points for class display work.

Please note that worksheets 8 and 27 comprise two facing pages; worksheets 8, 19 and 26 will need, in addition, the outline map of the British Isles and worksheets 15 and 18 will need the outline map of Europe (both maps are at the back of the book).

Below are some suggestions for follow-up and additional activities.

1. Activities linked to famous diarists (e.g. Samuel Pepys, Anne Frank) – research on these people and what they have to say. Biographies. A collection of newspaper cuttings could form a diary of events
2. Devise questionnaires and compare results. Discuss problems for historians in interpreting the results. Other problems of oral evidence could be discussed: e.g. bias and prejudice of the speaker, the effect of memory
3. Folk songs could also be considered
4. Consideration of other family trees, such as the British royal family; exercises to practise interpreting them. Create imaginary families
5. Comparison of Chinese, Christian, Islamic and Jewish calendars. The development of personal calendars or timelines
6. Pupils could bring in their own items for a class time capsule, which could be buried in the school grounds. Discuss the problems of preservation and the survival of historical evidence. Discuss the problems of interpreting artefacts and what they tell us of the civilisation that produced them
7. Conduct a survey of names within the school or in the area and analyse the patterns that emerge; display the results
8. Work with a dictionary of placenames to make maps showing original names and their meanings, graphs showing settlement patterns and types of settlements
9. Link the streetnames to architecture in the streets; is there a connection between style and names?
10. Drama to enact the hunt, considering the problems of the hunt. Collections of pictures of plants suitable for eating. Notes about the habitats of the plants collected. Modelling and painting on the theme of the hunt
11. Comparison with modern burial customs in different cultures. Graveyard surveys; rubbings in churches and churchyards
12. Research into other ancient scripts such as the Rosetta Stone. The pupils could devise their own script
13. Comparison with other calendars (e.g. North American Indian). Comparison of Roman gods with those of Greece or India. Biographies of the gods
14. Research into Roman warfare: work on great figures such as Caesar and Hannibal. Consideration of change and development by comparing medieval knights or modern soldiers with the Roman warriors
15. Find out about local Roman forts and their garrisons; use local museums. Consider how a Roman from one of these forts might have felt about his posting to Britain
16. Introduction to the abacus and Arabic numbers, perhaps making tallysticks. Invention of new codes for numbers and counting
17. Look at other forms of sea transport to show developments and change. Models and artwork
18. Comparisons with modern trade: pupils could draw maps to show where goods, bought locally, originate. Displays with food labels and packaging of goods
19. Fieldwork if possible. Collect postcards and photographs from tourist magazines for display to show features and development of castles. Research into living conditions
20. Modelling: build a motte and bailey castle. Draw up plans and decide on best methods of attack. Invent a siege game
21. Drama: research and enact the appointment of local lord – oaths of

allegiance and homage. Work out a system of government and services; compare with modern government
22. Drama: what happened when the commissioners visited your village? The results of the survey could be written up in medieval style and using quills
23. Modelling. Work on feudal dues and medieval village courts. A peasant's diary
24. Links with guilds and mystery plays – perhaps some acting. Comparisons with trades unions; work on the apprenticeship system
25. Work on modern punishment and the police; perhaps a talk by a local police officer
26. Plan a modern historical trip: where to go and why, maps and diagrams – guidebook-style accounts of places in the itinerary
27. Enquire into the heraldry of a local noble family, football club or other organisation such as scouts and guides
28. Study the local church in detail; rubbings, drawings, models, accounts of the building's history, biographies of famous people buried there. Work on transcripts of baptismal and burial registers
29. Research on travelling fairs, minstrels and games of chance and skill. Drama, display and frieze work. Discuss moral aspects of blood sports of past and present. Compare modern and medieval entertainments
30. Biographies of Henry VIII's wives. Study marriage customs of different cultures. Discuss ideas such as polygamy
31. Consider other traitors. Artwork connected to bonfire night. Study of other local and national festivals and their origins
32. Study of local epidemics of 19th century or earlier. Work on hospitals and nurses. Biographies of great men and women in medicine: Marie Curie, Alexander Fleming, Florence Nightingale, Louis Pasteur
33. Make a collection of herbs and study their uses. Drawings of local plants that might have had medicinal uses. Work on local witches or trials involving witchcraft in the past
34. Study the development of make-up and wigs, perhaps using the local museum or theatre. Artwork and modelling
35. Work on the local roads and turnpikes. Study of local canals. Biographies. Model sections of the different types of roads built in the 18th century
36. Drawings to illustrate the board for their own games. Research into highwaymen (e.g. Dick Turpin)
37. Study local farms. Use maps to show effects of enclosure on the landscape. Placenames of farms
38. Comparison with modern mining. Links with literature and folk songs. Work on mining disasters. Experiments to show how Davy lamps worked

All my own work

Throughout history people have kept diaries, writing down their thoughts and everyday events that happen to them. Diaries are important to historians because they give first hand accounts of the lives of rich, famous and ordinary people. There have been many famous diarists – Samuel Pepys, Sir Winston Churchill, Anne Frank – all of whom have given valuable information that helps to recreate the past.

1. In this lesson begin writing your own diary. Write down all the things that have happened to you over the last week. See how long you can keep writing your diary.

2. Draw pictures to make your diary more interesting.

3. Choose a story from the news. Keep a diary of events that take place.

4. As a class choose a topic from everyday life and build up a database of writing, pictures, photographs. You might choose modern fashion, music, your village or town. Remember: one day your work might be an important historical document.

PASS IT ON

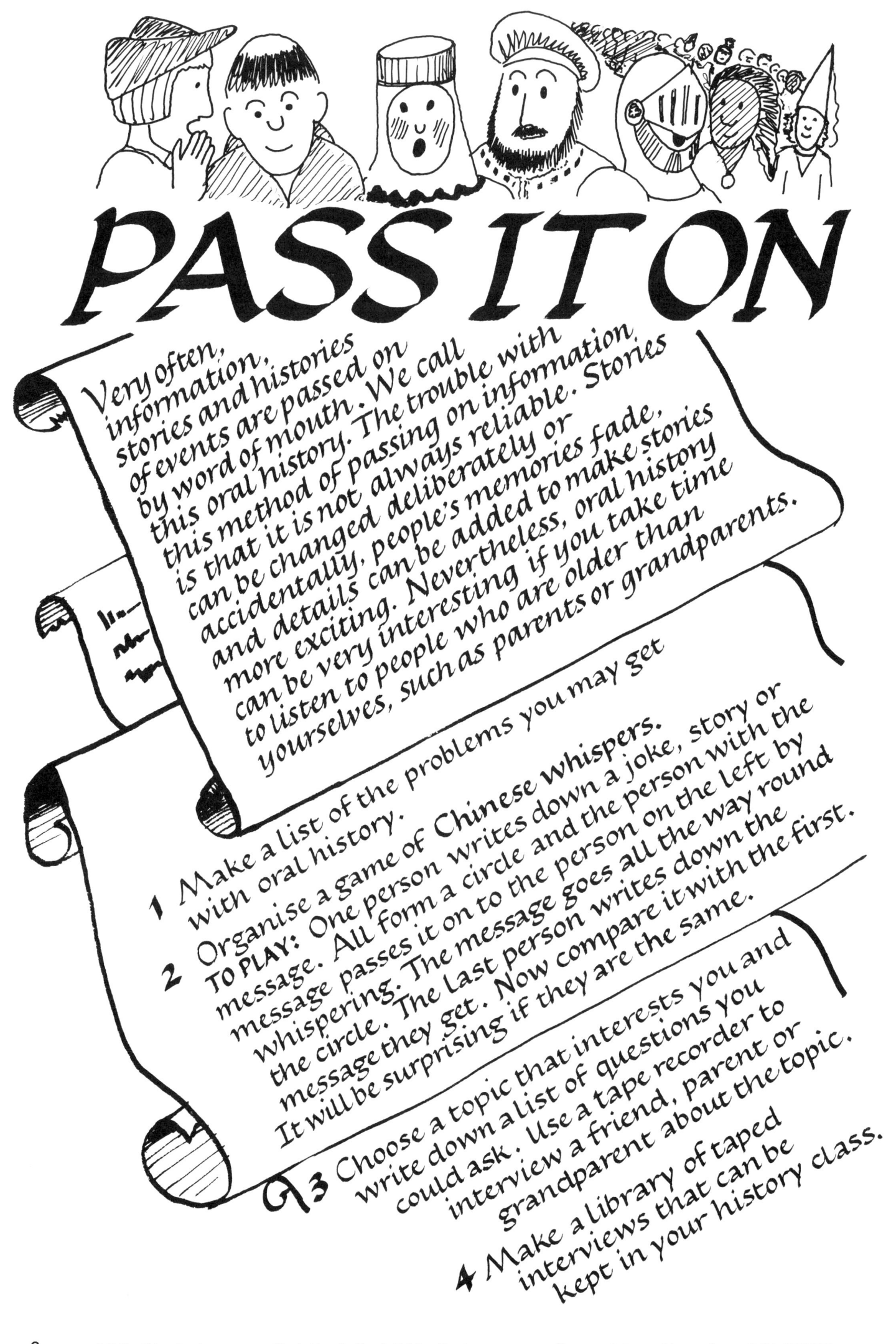

Very often, information, stories and histories of events are passed on by word of mouth. We call this oral history. The trouble with this method of passing on information is that it is not always reliable. Stories can be changed deliberately or accidentally, people's memories fade, and details can be added to make stories more exciting. Nevertheless, oral history can be very interesting if you take time to listen to people who are older than yourselves, such as parents or grandparents.

1. Make a list of the problems you may get with oral history.

2. Organise a game of Chinese Whispers.
TO PLAY: One person writes down a joke, story or message. All form a circle and the person with the message passes it on to the person on the left by whispering. The message goes all the way round the circle. The last person writes down the message they get. Now compare it with the first. It will be surprising if they are the same.

3. Choose a topic that interests you and write down a list of questions you could ask. Use a tape recorder to interview a friend, parent or grandparent about the topic.

4. Make a library of taped interviews that can be kept in your history class.

At our mother's knee

"Humpty Dumpty sat on the wall,
Humpty Dumpty had a great fall,
All the King's horses and all the King's men
Couldn't put Humpty together again."

Nursery rhymes, children's songs and invented games have always been a part of growing up. Each generation is taught the old rhymes, such as Humpty Dumpty and Jack and Jill; each new generation of children invents its own games and songs, especially playground games.

1. Give the nursery rhymes in the pictures their correct titles.
2. Draw a cartoon to tell the story of Humpty Dumpty.
3. Write down the names of the games that you play in the playground with your friends.
4. Write out any songs or chants that you use or have invented.
5. Draw a cartoon to illustrate your favourite nursery rhyme.

MEET the FAMILY

A FAMILY TREE

LOOK AT THIS FAMILY TREE

A family tree is a way of showing the different people who go to make up a family. It will show grandparents, brothers, sisters, aunts, uncles, cousins, nephews, nieces...

1 What is the relationship between JOHN and ANNE / JOHN and SIMON / JOHN and SUSAN?
2 How many nephews and nieces does MARIE have?
3 How many cousins has IAN?
4 What is the relationship between IAN and PAUL / IAN and PETER and SARAH?
5 What are the names of PAUL'S grandparents?
6 Think about your own family tree. Go back as far as you can.
7 Look again at the family tree. Think up ten questions about relationships.

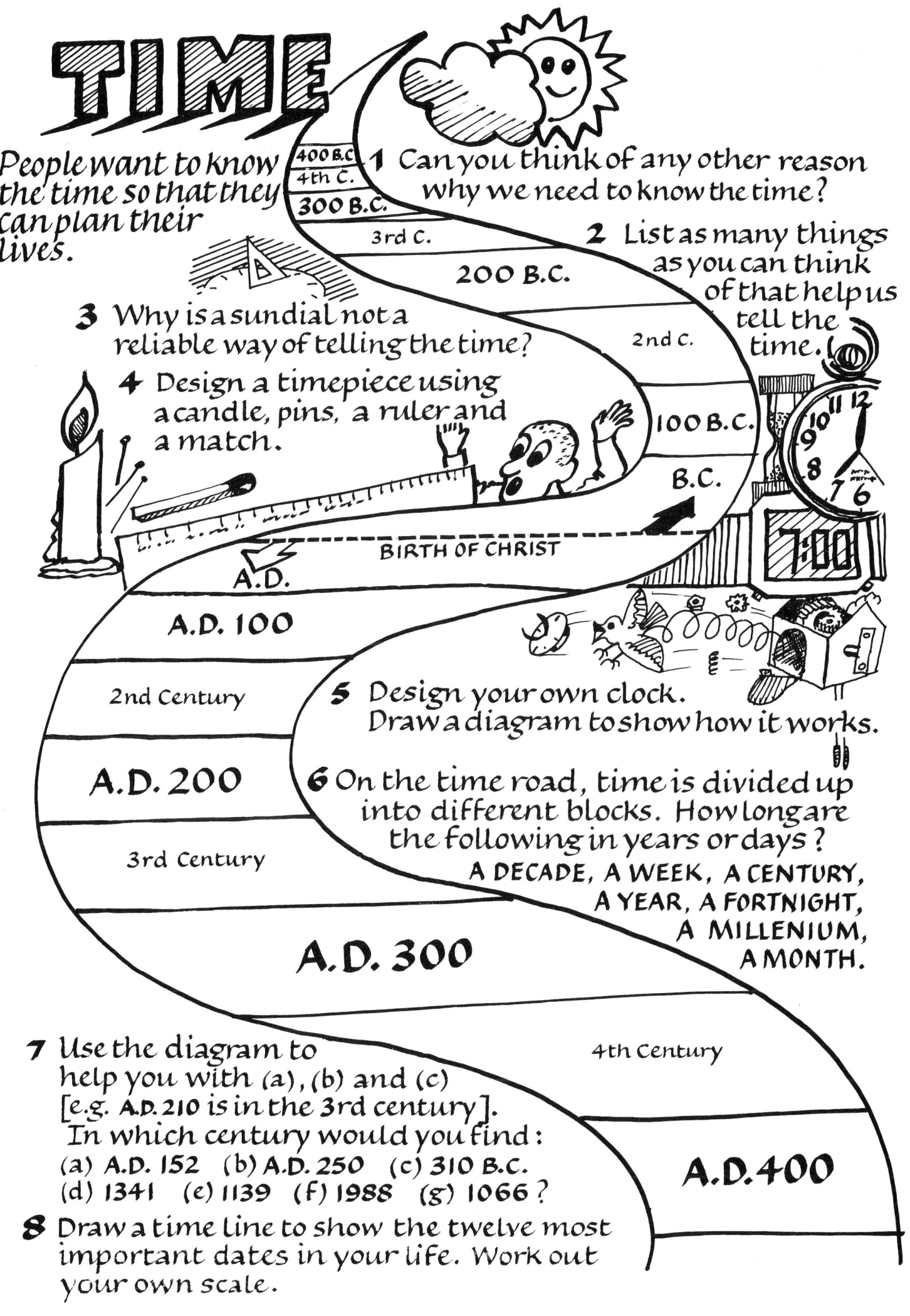

The governments of Earth have decided to send into outer space a spacecraft containing items that show best our life in the late 20th century. You have been chosen to be the historian attached to the Great Britain team – but what will you send into space?

1 On the spacecraft is a tape-recorded greetings message from you to aliens – write out a message you would like to record.

2 Design a flag to stand for Great Britain.

3 Make a list of items you would put into each of the cargo boxes shown ready to be loaded.

4 Imagine that the team's camera breaks down and there are still some items you want the aliens to know about. Describe in detail, as a historian, each of the following: – A TEAPOT
– YOUR NEIGHBOUR
– A RULER
– ANYTHING YOU LIKE (see if your neighbour recognises what you have described).

NAMES and more NAMES

Up to the Middle Ages most people were known by their first name, but as time went by a second or surname was added. This might have shown a person's relationship to another – ROBERT<u>SON</u> was Robert's son.

Sometimes the job title was added to the first name – John the shepherd became **JOHN SHEPHERD**.

On other occasions a nickname stuck to become the surname. Often physical appearance was used to distinguish a person from the neighbours. **TALL** or **REDHEAD** are examples of this type of name. Their birthplace sometimes gave people their name, e.g. Sally **YORK**.

THINGS TO DO

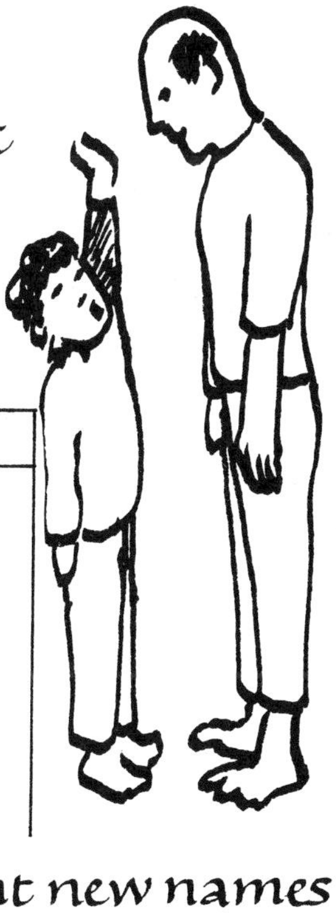

1. Here is a list of names. Put them under the right heading:

   SAWYER   ROUND   SMITH
   LONDON   SMALL   WALKER   CARPENTER   YORK
   WILSON   FARMER   JACKSON   HULL   CLERK
   RICHARDSON   BRIGHT   LEEDS

OCCUPATION	PLACE	APPEARANCE	RELATIONSHIP

2. Think carefully about five of your friends. Invent new names for them. Can your neighbour recognise the people?
3. Find out what these surnames mean; they are all connected with jobs. A good dictionary will help.   CROPPER, FLETCHER, TINKER, CHAPMAN, TANNER, WEAVER, TAYLOR, CLERK

WHAT'S IN A NAME?

U.K. MAP REQD.

All words and place names have a meaning. They tell us about the people who settled the land and what it was like at the time. Sometimes we can learn the names of the people who owned the land.

Here are some examples:

OXFORD – Village by the ford for oxen.
HASTINGS – Village of Haesta's people.
FOULSHAM – Village of Fugol's home.
CROPSTON – Village by Cropp's home.
FIRBY – Frithi's village.
THORNTHORPE – Torgrim's farm.

<u>You will need the placenames information sheet to answer these questions</u>

1. Find a map of Britain. Look for ten places that end in **CHESTER**. Mark these on your outline map. In what period were these places started?

2. Make up ten placenames of your own. Explain what each name means.

3. Using a detailed map (such as an O.S. map), try to work out when most of the villages in your home area received their names.

4. Find a local road map. Plan a short tour around your home area. Make a list of the places you go through. Show their origin and meaning.

(You will need an outline map, a local map, an atlas and, if possible, a dictionary of placenames.)

PLACENAMES

Placenames tell us when a place received its name – as in the tables below.

CELTIC
(before A.D. 400)
- -con - hill
- -pen - hill/head
- -aber } river mouth
- -inver }
- -perth - harbour
- -caer - fortress

ROMAN
(A.D. 43-400)
- -chester } fortified place, or city
- -cester }
- -caster }
- -street - paved way

SCANDINAVIAN
NORSE & DANE
(A.D. 800-1100)
- -toft - homestead
- -kirk - church
- -by - village
- -beck - stream
- -thorpe - settlement

ANGLO-SAXON
(A.D. 450-1100)
- -ing - land of people
- -ham - homestead
- -ford - ford
- -worth } clearing in a wood
- -ley }
- -ton - hedged enclosure
- -bury } fortified place
- -borough }

Streetnames often give clues to the past. Sometimes a street was named after a famous person or event. Sometimes a street might be called after some feature in it, such as a church. Occasionally streets are named after other towns. Here are the names of some streets in

YORK: ALMA TERRACE, BRIGHT STREET, HUDSON STREET, MERCHANTGATE, JEWBURY, DAVYGATE, CHURCH STREET, SPURRIERGATE.

Using a streetmap or town directory, fill in the table below with streetnames in your town or village. (If you live in a large city, choose only a part that interests you, such as the city centre or the area around your home.)

STREETS IN _____

PERSON	TRADE	EVENT	CHURCH/SAINT

1 Which is the most common type of street name? Draw a graph to show the results of your research.

2 Choose two street names and try to find out more about their origins.

3 If you were naming streets in your town today, which events or people would you choose?

Finding Food
STONE-AGE STYLE

Before 10 000 B.C. people were not farmers but found their food by hunting and gathering wild berries and plants. This meant that they moved around following herds of animals or looking for new plants. Settlements were temporary and often in places where different tribes met. The banks of rivers or lakesides were excellent sites for hunter/gatherers.

You will need to use reference books and your powers of deduction to answer the questions.

1 What sorts of animals could Stone Age people have hunted? Make a list.
2 What plants or fruits could you gather in the countryside today?
3 How would you hunt an animal as large as a mammoth or bison? These words might help: pit, cliff, spears, fire, drive, stones, noise.
4 Find out all you can about hunter/gatherers today. The best examples are the Bushmen of the Kalahari Desert or the Australian Aborigines.

In pre-Christian times people believed that they needed to take some of their belongings with them to the next world. Burials have always been marked with tombs or graves. Sometimes these were built to look like houses, as in the Middle East. In Egypt pyramids were built, while in Britain mounds of earth were constructed. During the Neolithic period bodies were buried together in long mounds but around 2500 B.C. customs changed and cremation became fashionable.

Human remains were buried under round mounds or barrows.

You will need a dictionary and some reference books to answer these questions

1 What items would be buried with the following: **A FARMER, A WARRIOR, A WOMAN, A PRIEST**? Show your answer in a table like this —

PERSON	ITEMS IN GRAVE
King	Crown, shield, jewels, armour

2 Find out about Egyptian funeral customs. Look up pyramids and mummies in reference books and write a paragraph about them.

3 Find out what the following terms mean: **TUMULUS, NEOLITHIC, CREMATION, SARCOPHAGUS, EMBALMING.**

THE SECRET OF THE PHARAOHS

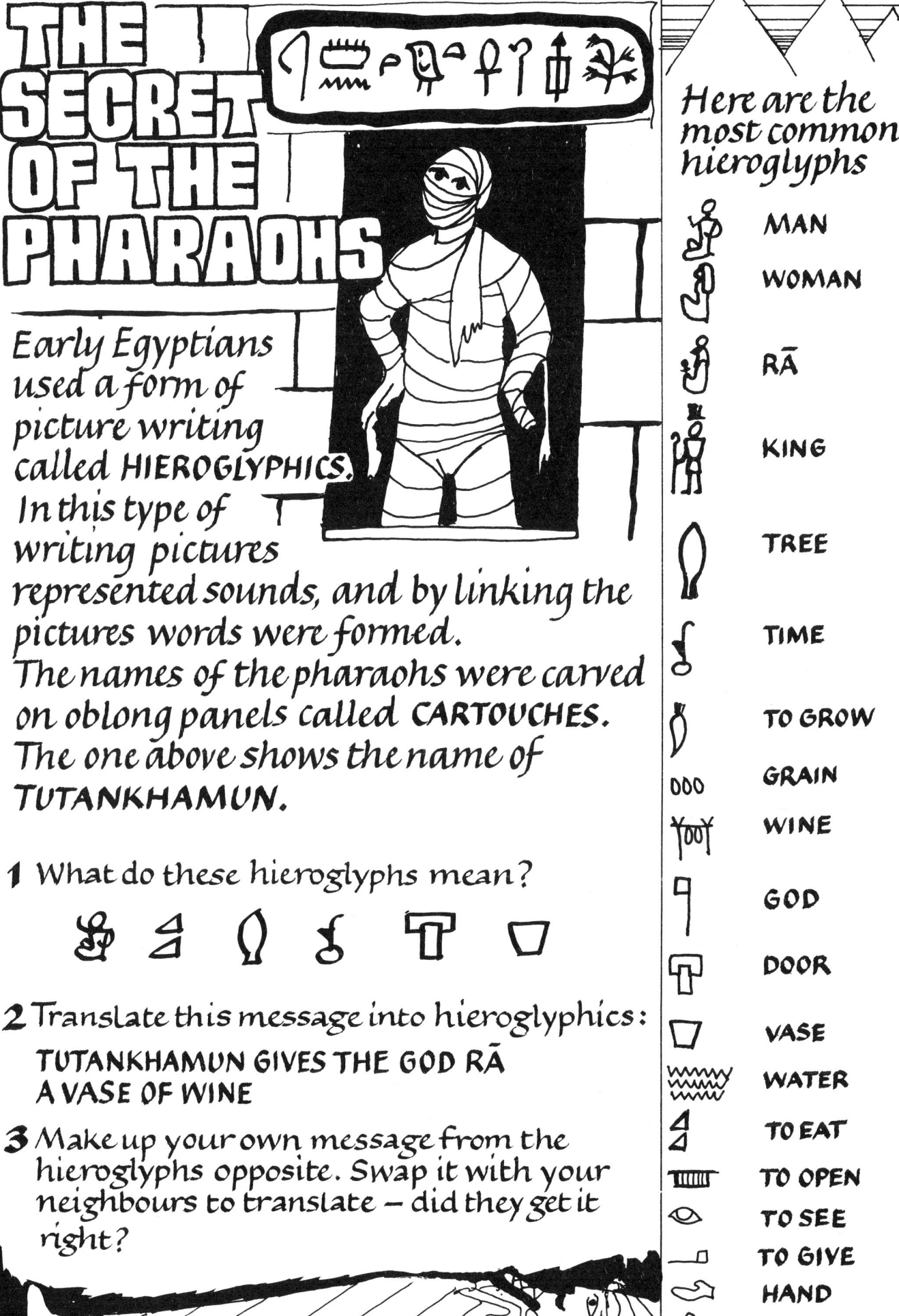

Early Egyptians used a form of picture writing called **HIEROGLYPHICS**. In this type of writing pictures represented sounds, and by linking the pictures words were formed. The names of the pharaohs were carved on oblong panels called **CARTOUCHES**. The one above shows the name of **TUTANKHAMUN**.

1 What do these hieroglyphs mean?

2 Translate this message into hieroglyphics:
   TUTANKHAMUN GIVES THE GOD RĀ A VASE OF WINE

3 Make up your own message from the hieroglyphs opposite. Swap it with your neighbours to translate — did they get it right?

Here are the most common hieroglyphs

- MAN
- WOMAN
- RĀ
- KING
- TREE
- TIME
- TO GROW
- GRAIN
- WINE
- GOD
- DOOR
- VASE
- WATER
- TO EAT
- TO OPEN
- TO SEE
- TO GIVE
- HAND
- A

MONTH BY MONTH

7 SEPT. 8 OCT. NOV. 9 DEC. 10
After numbers

JANUARY
After JANUS, the two-faced god who looked back into the old year and forward into the new

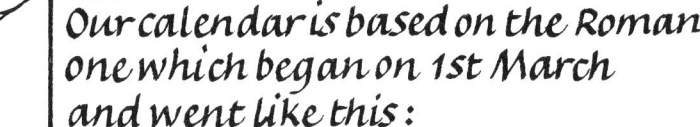

FEBRUARY
After the Roman festival of Februa

AUGUST
After Augustus, the first emperor of Rome

Our calendar is based on the Roman one which began on 1st March and went like this:

MARTIUS	MARCH
APRILIS	APRIL
MAIUS	MAY
IUNIUS	JUNE
QUINTILIS	5th MONTH
SEXTILIS	6th MONTH
SEPTEMBER	SEPTEMBER (SEPT = 7)
OCTOBER	OCTOBER (OCT = 8)
NOVEMBER	NOVEMBER (NOV = 9)
DECEMBER	DECEMBER (DECEM = 10)
IANUARIUS	JANUARY
FEBRUARIUS	FEBRUARY

BUT In 46 B.C. Julius Caesar reformed the calendar. The year now began in January and the name of the fifth month became July in honour of Julius Caesar.

MARCH
After the god of war (spring battles with winter!)

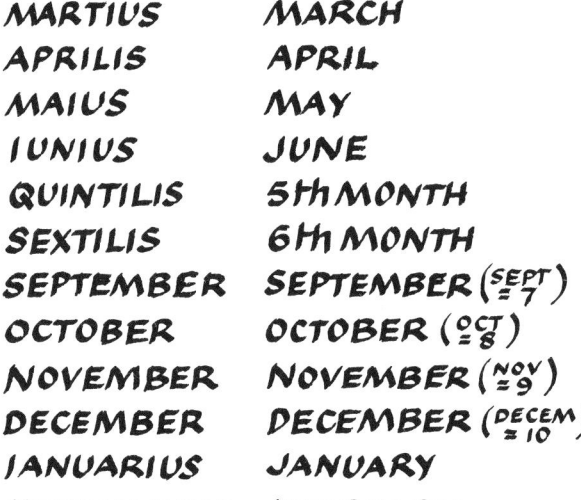

JULY
After Julius Caesar

JUNE
After Juno, wife of the king of the gods

MAY
After Maia, the mother goddess (many animals give birth this month)

APRIL
After Aprilis, another name for the goddess of love (many animals mate at this time)

The old sixth month became August in honour of the Emperor Augustus. This meant that the rest of the months were two out. They still are: September, the early Roman seventh month, is our ninth month, and so on.

1 Make up your own calendar: draw a diagram to illustrate each of the months. Invent new names for the months.

2 Our calendar begins with the birth of Christ. **FIND OUT**: what A.D. and B.C. mean; when the Roman calendar began; the date and event that began the Jewish calendar.

3 Calendars begin with events that are of special importance. What three events in the last 100 years do you think would be suitable for starting a new calendar?

4 Look up in your reference books the Roman gods mentioned above and write a paragraph about each of them.

THE MEAN MACHINE
A ROMAN SOLDIER AND HIS EQUIPMENT

Roman legionaries were highly trained and well equipped. Their armour, made out of metal strips, was very flexible and could move easily while protecting the most exposed parts of their bodies. They carried two throwing spears, a short stabbing sword and a shield. While on the march they carried food for 14 days and equipment. In addition, each man carried one or two 2-metre posts to help to build a fence round the camp at night.

HERE IS A LIST OF EQUIPMENT

LATIN	ENGLISH	LATIN	ENGLISH
PILUM	SPEAR	GLADUS	SWORD
GALEA	HELMET	PUGGIO	DAGGER
BALTEAUS	BELT	LONICA	BREASTPLATE
SCUTUM	SHIELD	TUNICA	TUNIC
CALIGA	BOOT	BRACAE	BREECHES

THINGS TO DO

1 On the figure mark the equipment of a legionary in English or Latin.

2 Unscramble these items of equipment, then write out their Latin names:
RASPE, DOWRS, NITUC, GARDEG, MELTEH.

3 Imagine that you are a legionary. Describe and explain your equipment.

4 Using reference books, find out how the Roman army was organised.

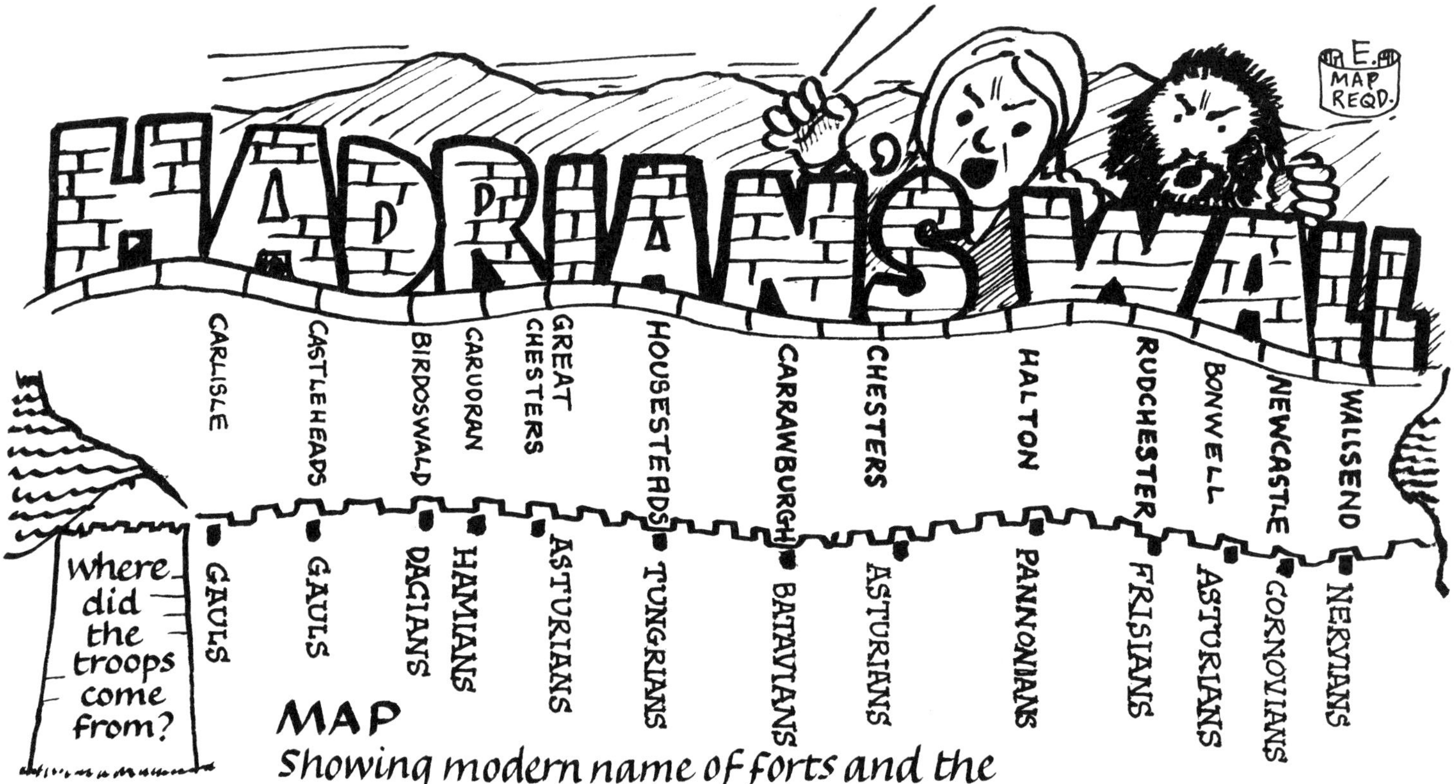

HADRIAN'S WALL

MAP — Showing modern name of forts and the races of Roman soldiers who garrisoned them.

Forts (left to right): CARLISLE, CASTLEHEADS, BIRDOSWALD, CARVORAN, GREAT CHESTERS, HOUSESTEADS, CARRAWBURGH, CHESTERS, HALTON, RUDCHESTER, BONWELL, NEWCASTLE, WALLSEND

Garrisons (left to right): GAULS, GAULS, DACIANS, HAMIANS, ASTURIANS, TUNGRIANS, BATAVIANS, ASTURIANS, PANNONIANS, FRISIANS, ASTURIANS, CORNOVIANS, NERVIANS

Where did the troops come from?

In A.D. 120 the Emperor Hadrian decided a wall 73 miles long should be built to cut off the barbarians of Caledonia (Scotland) from the Britons who lived under Roman rule. He thought this would bring peace. Troops were brought from all over the Empire to defend the barrier.

MODERN NAME	ROMAN NAME	KEY
BELGIANS	NERVIANS	
BRITISH	CORNOVIANS	
SPANIARDS	ASTURIANS	
HUNGARIANS	PANNONIANS	
DUTCH (N. COAST)	FRISIANS	
DUTCH	BATAVIANS	
BELGIANS (NORTH)	TUNGRIANS	
SYRIANS	HAMIANS	
ROMANIANS	DACIANS	
FRENCH	GAULS	

1 Add a colour key to the list of names on the table. Now, using these colours, shade in on your outline map the countries where the soldiers come from.

2 Write a paragraph explaining who thought of the wall; say why and when it was built.

3 Find a map of Britain in your atlas. Look for the line of the wall between **NEWCASTLE** and **CARLISLE**. Why do you think that the wall was built on this route?

4 Do you think that the wall solved the problem of defending the country?

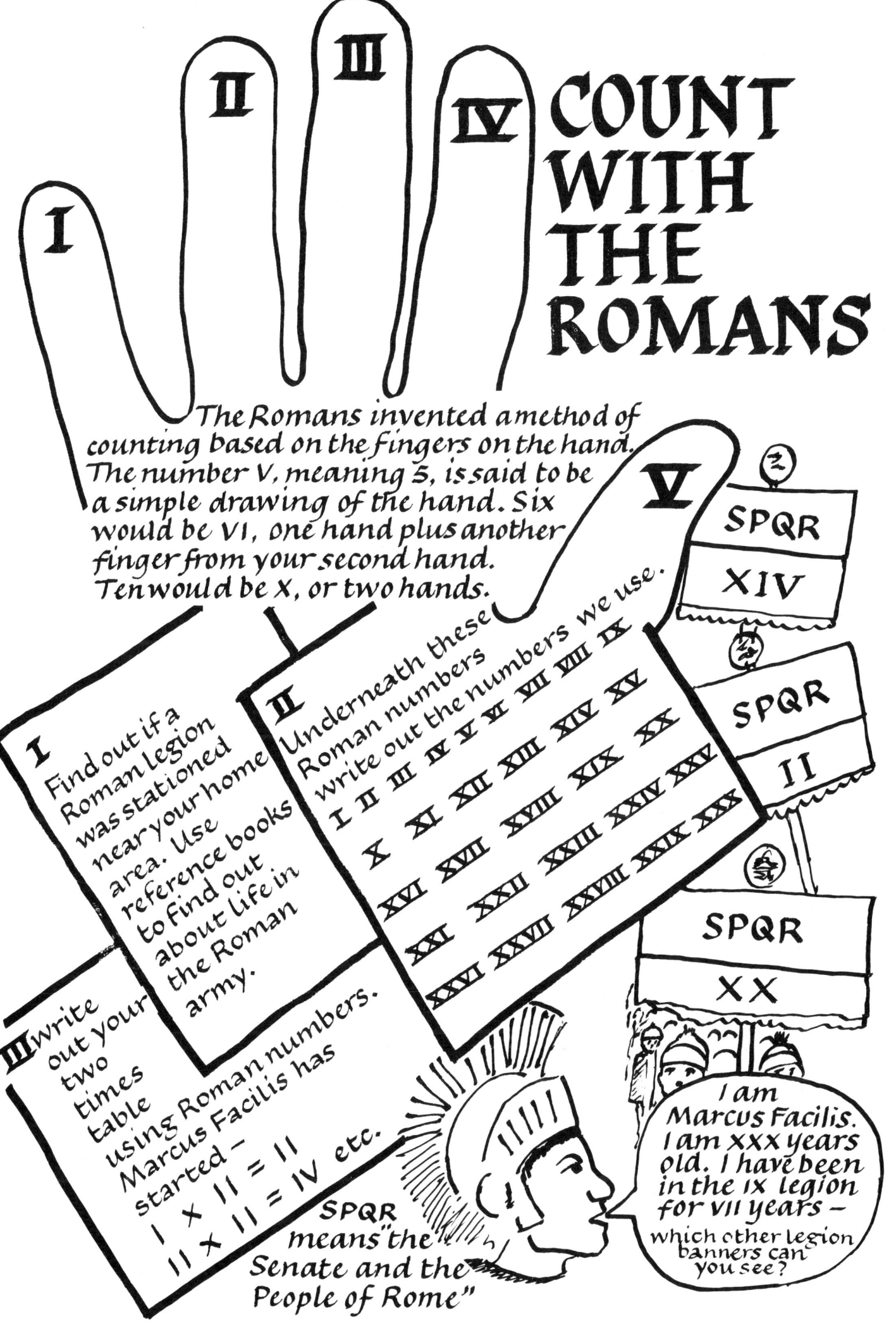

SAIL AWAY

The Vikings from Scandinavia were great seafarers. Travelling in their longships they were feared throughout Europe. Their ships, nearly 24½ metres long, were powered by oars and a great square sail with a striped or simple pattern on it. These boats could sail up rivers. Men sat on sea chests and stored their few belongings under loose floorboards. There was little protection. At the prow of the ship a fearsome dragonhead looked down to frighten man and spirit. The pride of the sailors was shown by the names of their ships, such as "rider of water" and "greyhound of the seas".

WHAT TO DO

1 Colour the drawing of the longship. Then add these labels to your picture: FLAG or WEATHER VANE, MAST, DRAGONHEAD, PROW, SQUARE SAIL, STEERING OAR, SHIELDS

2 Design a dragonhead prow for a Viking ship. Make it as frightening as possible.

3 What would you call your ship if you were a Viking? Label yours.

VIKING TRADERS

YOU WILL NEED THE OUTLINE MAP OF EUROPE

1. Find and colour in NORWAY, DENMARK and SWEDEN. These were VIKING homelands.
2. Now mark in the following: ENGLAND, ICELAND, RUSSIA, RIVER DNIEPER, and also the major Viking cities of LONDON, DUBLIN, YORK, OSLO, KIEV, STOCKHOLM. Add the cities of ROME and CONSTANTINOPLE.

VOYAGES

3. First draw an arrow by sea from NORWAY to ICELAND. Then draw an arrow by sea from SCANDINAVIA to BRITAIN. From BRITAIN draw an arrow by sea round SPAIN, into the MEDITERRANEAN SEA and to GREECE.
4. The SWEDISH VIKINGS took the EASTERN route. From SWEDEN draw an arrow across the sea and overland to KIEV, then down the DNIEPER RIVER to the BLACK SEA and through to CONSTANTINOPLE.

Study this list, which shows some of the goods and countries with which the Vikings traded.

GREENLAND
WALRUS IVORY, FURS, HIDES, WOOLLENS.

BRITAIN
WHEAT, HONEY, TIN, WOOLLENS.

FRANCE
SALT, WINE.

RUSSIA
WINE, SLAVES, POTTERY, GLASS, WEAPONS, CLOTH, JEWELS.

BYZANTINE EMPIRE
SILK, FRUIT, WINE, JEWELS, SILVER, SPICES.

5. Now unscramble these goods and say which countries they come from: SAGLS, TAWHE, KILS, NIT, LATS, RESVIL, YENHO.

CASTLES

WHERE SHALL WE BUILD THEM?

After the Norman Conquest the Normans had to protect what they had won. To control the Saxons they needed strongly protected places – so they built **CASTLES**.

AIMS OF THE CASTLE BUILDERS

- To stop invasion.
- To control trade and movement. Their castles had to be in places they could easily defend.

1 Find and write on the map:
NEWCASTLE, YORK, DURHAM, LONDON, LINCOLN, CHESTER, EXETER, CHEPSTOW, CARLISLE, SCARBOROUGH, NORWICH, DOVER.

2 What sort of site would you look for if you were building **CASTLES**? Think about defending against attack!

3 Look at the aims of the castle builders. Now choose words from the list to complete this sentence –
"In order to keep a grip on the country, the **NORMANS** built **CASTLES** in the following places ....."

PORTS, LARGE TOWNS, RIVER CROSSINGS, VILLAGES, BORDERS, VALLEYS, FORESTS, MOORLANDS, MOUNTAINS

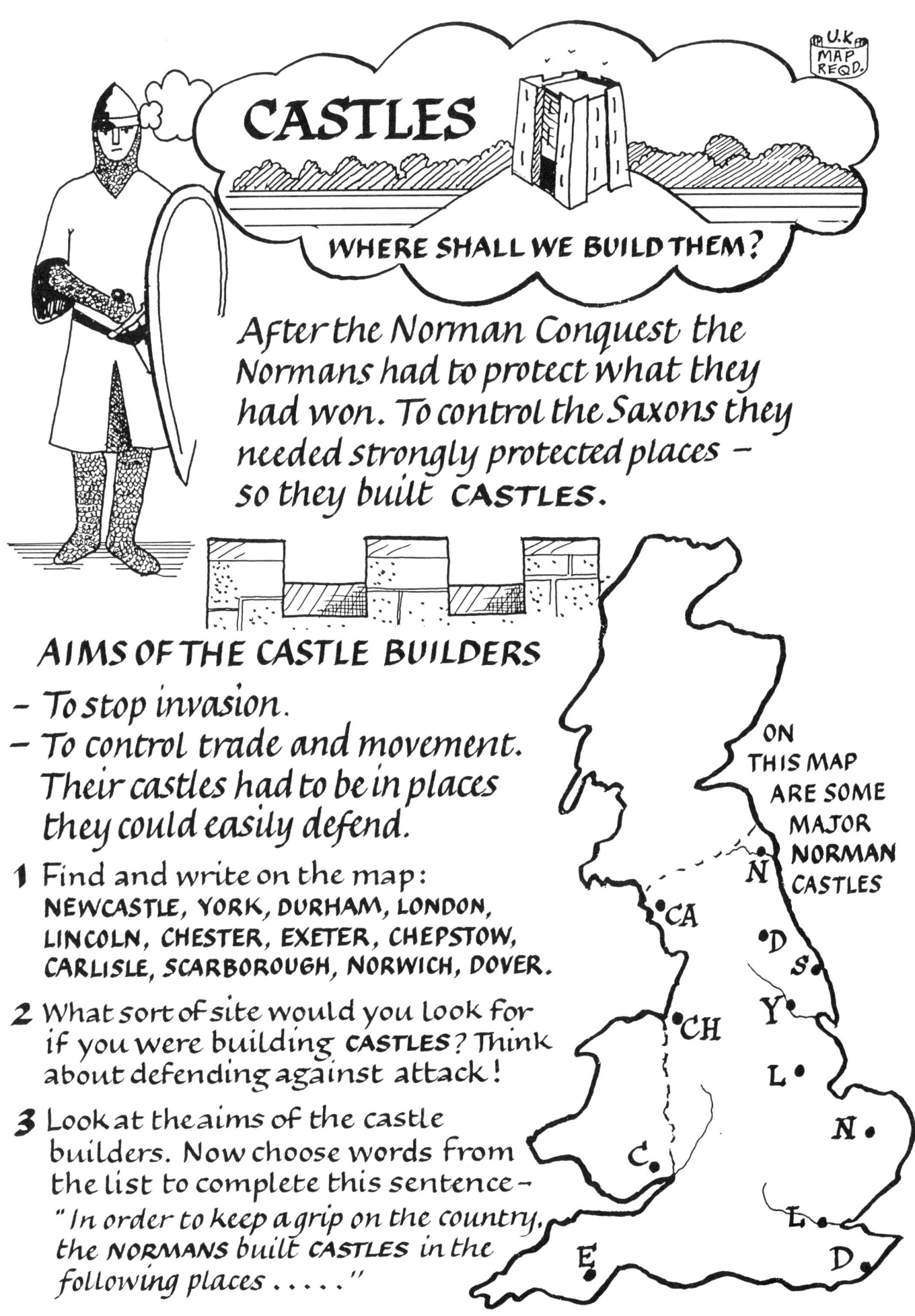

ON THIS MAP ARE SOME MAJOR NORMAN CASTLES

ATTACK!

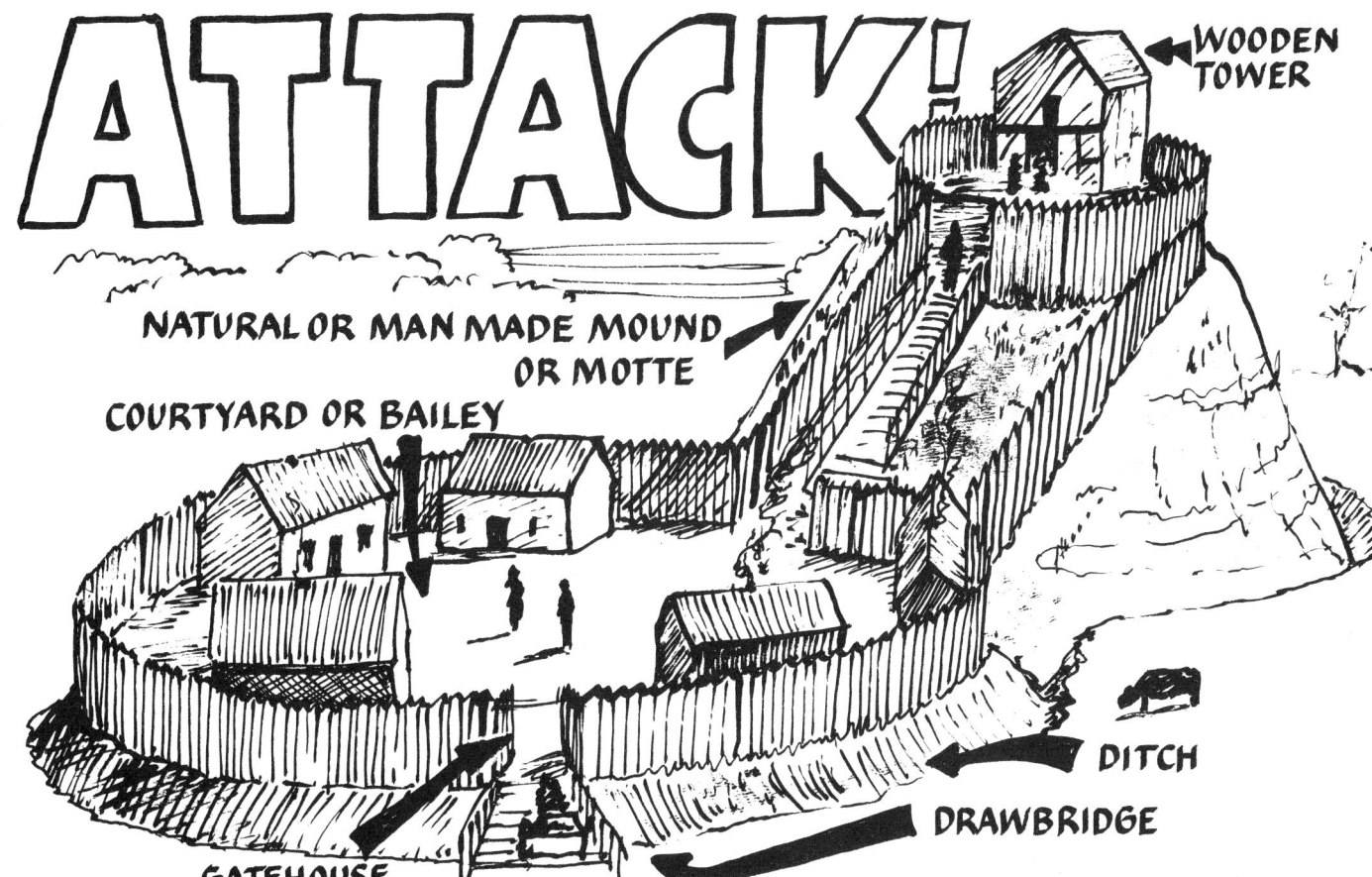

After the **BATTLE OF HASTINGS** in 1066, William the Conqueror needed to make sure that England remained peaceful. He did this by building hundreds of castles throughout the country. Loyal soldiers from each castle would stop anyone in the area from rebelling. The earliest type of castle was a simple but quickly erected fortification called a **MOTTE AND BAILEY** castle.

A castle was a centre of military power and local government and a safe place in times of trouble.

1 Why was this type of castle called **MOTTE AND BAILEY**?

2 What are the advantages of this type of castle?

3 What are the disadvantages of this type of castle?

4 Imagine that you are a Baron planning to attack the castle in the picture. Write a story explaining how you would attack.

I'll scratch your back if you'll scratch mine

During the Middle Ages there was too much land in Britain for the King to control by himself.

THE KING — To protect the country and rule fairly

TO THE BARON — Loyalty and obedience to the King. Provide King with soldiers, money and accommodation. Protect and care for knights.

TO THE KNIGHT — Obey Baron. Provide him with money, soldiers and food. Protect serfs.

TO THE SERF — Work on the Baron's land. Give food to King each year. Pay tax. Fight and never leave the village.

The King granted land to about 200 Barons in return for their support and loyalty. The Barons, having the same problem as the King, granted land to their followers, their Knights. The Barons and Knights together organised the running of the countryside and the control of serfs. This was known as the FEUDAL system.

1. Why did the King need to share out his kingdom with the Barons?
2. Why do you think that loyalty was important in making the feudal system work?
3. What might happen if you had a weak King and strong Barons?
4. In your own words say how the feudal system worked.
5. Explain what people did for one another.

DOMESDAY

In 1086 William the Conqueror needed money. In order to tax people, he decided to find out who held land and its worth.

He wanted to know:

The name of the place?
Who held it in King Edward's time?
Who held it in 1086?
How big was the area?
How many plough teams did it support?
How many villagers?
How much woodland and pasture?
How much was it worth before 1066, in 1066 and in 1086?

Royal officers rode round the country asking these questions. A little while later more officials checked up by asking the same questions. This information was recorded in a book known as the Domesday book.

1. Write a short paragraph describing why the King had a survey made and explain what he wanted to know.
2. How would you have checked the accuracy of the information?
3. With a friend, make a list of questions you would ask for a modern Domesday book. How would you organise the collection of information?
4. Try to find the answers to some of your questions.

The Three Field Trick

Until the 18th century, most of England's farming was based on a **THREE FIELD SYSTEM** of crop rotation. Each village farmed three large fields divided into strips about 183 metres long by 20 metres wide. The land was shared out between the villagers according to their importance. Each year one field had to be left to rest. This was called leaving the field **FALLOW**. Being mainly self-supporting, the villagers had to make the most of the land around them.

1. How could the wood, marsh, rough pasture and meadowland be used by the villagers?
2. Imagine you are **HAROLD**; what problems do you face farming your land?
3. What was the approximate area of each strip of land?
4. If **SIMON** was an inefficient farmer, why might this cause problems for **GEOFFREY**?
5. Why do you think one field was left fallow each year?

The men from the Guildhall

In Medieval towns GUILDS looked after the interests of the townspeople and the craftsmen, merchants and tradesmen who served them. Guildsmen controlled the quality of work and punished craftsmen who sold poor quality goods, bakers who put chalk in their bread, innkeepers who watered ale or fishmongers who sold rotten fish. BEWARE!

In towns like York and Chester, the Guilds would come together on Corpus Christi day in June to put on an open air pageant telling the story of Jesus from birth to resurrection.

1. How did the Guilds look after their members?
2. How did the Guilds protect townspeople from bad workmanship?
3. Why do you think that Guilds stopped work by candlelight?
4. Imagine that you are an inspector from the butchers' Guild. Write a short play about the sale of rotten meat. What happens to the butcher? You can make the play serious or funny.

FAIR COP GOV

During the Middle Ages there was no police force and until 1166 no system of trial by jury. This did not mean that criminals went unpunished; in fact punishments were quite barbaric. People were tried by ordeal; their hands could be plunged into boiling water and if the burns healed in three days they were found innocent. If guilty, criminals could be hanged from gibbets or gallows, placed in the stocks or even banished from the country. Thieves often had ears, fingers or hands chopped off!

1. How are people in the pictures being punished? Which of the punishments would not be allowed today and why?
2. Use a reference book to find out more about trials by ordeal. Why was this type of trial unfair?
3. Can you think of any crimes committed today that could NOT have been committed in the Middle Ages?

THE PILGRIM

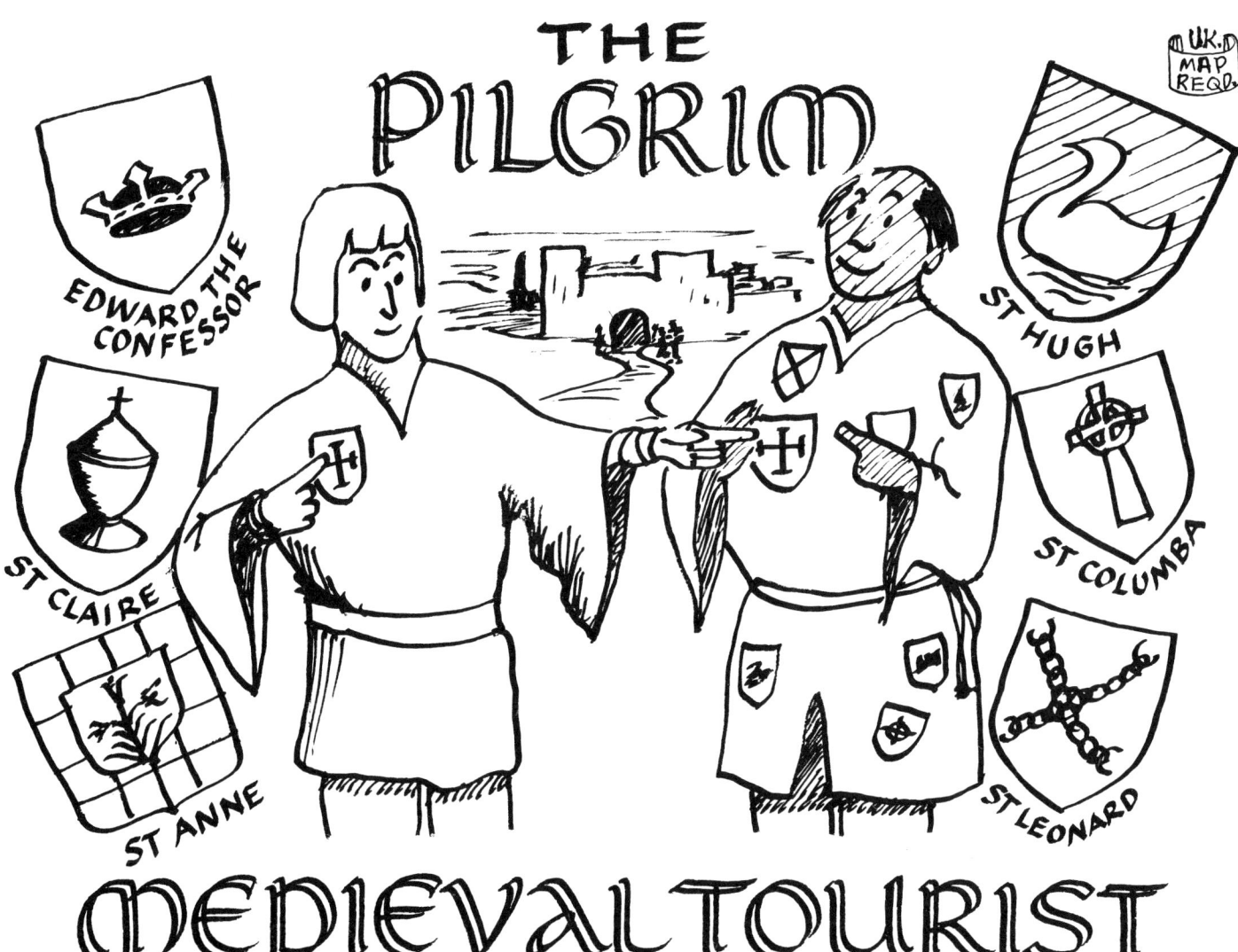

MEDIEVAL TOURIST

During the Middle Ages pilgrimages to places where holy objects were kept were very popular. Some pilgrims went to pray for a cure for sickness, others went for luck or to give thanks. Pilgrims usually went in groups for fear of robbers. They often collected badges to sew onto their clothes to show where they had been. Pilgrims to St Hugh of Lincoln had a swan badge.

You will need an outline map of Britain and an atlas

1. Mark on the map places that were popular with pilgrims: **CANTERBURY, DURHAM, ST ALBANS, LINCOLN, BURY ST EDMUNDS, WALSINGHAM, GLASTONBURY, YORK**
2. Design a badge for a saint of your choice.
3. Write a paragraph explaining a pilgrim's journey to a holy place.
4. Try to find at least two places where people go on pilgrimage today. Explain why they go there.

Identify Yourself
Heraldry & Coats of Arms
INFORMATION SHEET

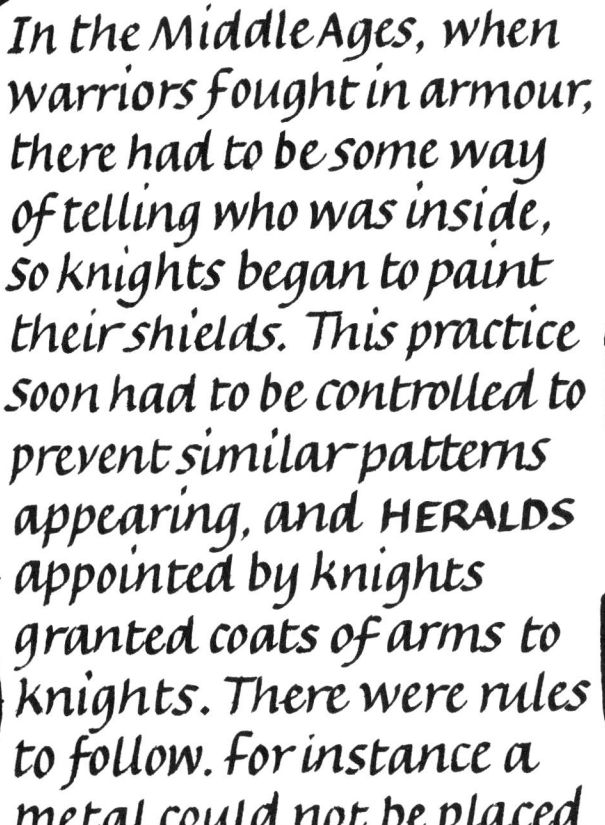

In the Middle Ages, when warriors fought in armour, there had to be some way of telling who was inside, so knights began to paint their shields. This practice soon had to be controlled to prevent similar patterns appearing, and HERALDS appointed by knights granted coats of arms to knights. There were rules to follow. For instance a metal could not be placed on a metal nor a colour upon a colour. Sometimes a man might choose a pun for his shield. A shepherd might have a sheep on his shield.

Heraldic Colours

METALS: OR – GOLD, ARGENT – SILVER. AZURE – BLUE, GULES – RED, VERT – GREEN, SABLE – BLACK, PURPURE – PURPLE.

Identify Yourself
Heraldry & Coats of Arms

ACTIVITY SHEET

USING THE INFORMATION SHEET...

1. Design your own shield. It may be divided into halves or quarters and each part may be different. This usually happened when families were joined by marriage.

2. Draw symbols to show the following names: **WALKER, BIRD, FLETCHER, WHEELER.**

3. Look around your town and try to find any shields on public buildings or churches. Make some sketches and try to find whose coats of arms they were.

4. Does your town have a coat of arms? If so, find out what it is, draw and describe it.

Look in the church

SAINT SEBASTIAN

SAINT AMBROSE

SAINT CYRIL

SAINT CLEMENT

Few people could read or write in the Middle Ages. Churches therefore acted as glorious picture books which helped people to understand the stories of the Bible. Walls were painted, glass stained and carvings looked down from every angle.

Many figures in church carried emblems or symbols to show who they were.

1 Design symbols for these Christian figures – use the information to help.

> **ST STEPHEN** – was stoned to death.
> **ST SWITHUN** – if it rains on his day we get 40 days of rain!
> **ST PETER** – he was given the keys to Heaven.
> **ST LEONARD** – is the patron saint of prisoners.
> **ST CRISPIN** – is the patron saint of shoemakers.

2 Try to arrange a visit to a local church. Try to find symbols and saints. Make sketches and notes. Try to find out who the figures are.

3 Look up the name of the saint of a local church in a directory of saints and write about him or her.

THAT'S ENTERTAINMENT

A wide variety of sports, games and entertainments gave people in the Middle Ages time to relax and enjoy themselves. Children still played their own invented games like hide and seek, tig and marbles, much the same as today. For adults there was football, archery or the quieter game of chess, or just listening to minstrels playing trumpets, gitterns, harps and sackbuts.

The more bloodthirsty could go to bearbaiting rings or to watch cockfighting whilst others could watch religious actors perform mystery plays or travelling actors called mummers playing in the street.

1. Describe the different games and pastimes you can see on the page. Which of them would be banned today? Explain why.
2. Can you work out which pastimes and entertainments are jumbled up here?
   UGGILGJN   IGFCKOICTHGN   ESCHS   RYCRHAE
   ABRLMSE   AIDNCGN   IGKTASN   LALOTOBF
3. Make a list of games, hobbies and pastimes you enjoy.

Have you met the wife?

In 1509, at the age of 17, Henry VIII became King of England, a position he kept until his death in 1547.

During his reign, Henry married six women. He divorced two, had two beheaded, one died and one outlived him.

Anne Boleyn — BEHEADED

Jane Seymour — DIED

Anne of Cleves — DIVORCED

Catherine of Aragon — DIVORCED

Catherine Howard — BEHEADED

Catherine Parr — OUTLIVED HIM

For royalty marriage was a matter of business, and for Henry it was a search for a wife who would give birth to a son as heir to the English throne.

1 Use the cartoon and information in the introduction to do the crossword.

ACROSS
1) Outlived Henry.
5) Only wife called this.
6) The monarch.
7) Being married to Henry, she died. Naturally.
8) This Cathy went for the chop.

DOWN
2) Lost her head over Henry.
3) This Cathy was divorced.
4) Divorced.

2 Choose one of Henry's six wives; use a reference book to find out more about her life.

Remember Remember

"Remember Remember the 5th of November, gunpowder, treason and plot. I see no reason why gunpowder treason should ever be forgot."

CAPTIONS On the 4th of November 1605 Guy Fawkes was arrested in the cellars under the House of Lords. Guy Fawkes was one member of a plot to blow up Parliament on its state opening by James I the following day.

- 1603: James I became King and began persecuting catholics.
- Guy Fawkes plots with others to blow up the House of Lords.
- A tunnel is begun under the House of Lords but abandoned.
- Plotters rent a cellar under the House of Lords and hide 36 barrels of gunpowder.
- One plotter warns Lord Montague of plot. The King is warned.
- Night of NOVEMBER 4th: cellars searched. Fawkes arrested.
- Other plotters are rounded up and hanged, drawn and quartered.

1 Use the captions to draw your own strip cartoon telling the gunpowder plot story.
2 Write a story about your own November 5th celebrations.
3 Find out what the words TREASON and CONSPIRACY mean.
4 Find out what HANGED, DRAWN AND QUARTERED means.

Ring o' Ring o' Roses

In 1665, England was in the grip of a terrible disease called the Bubonic Plague. The Plague killed so many people that it was called the "Great Plague". The rose-red rash and sneezing that were part of this illness gave rise to the singing game "ring o' ring o' roses". The disease was spread by fleas that lived on rats – rats that thrived on the filthy overcrowded conditions in towns and cities. Today the Plague is preventable and curable because we have the knowledge, technology and medicine to understand and combat the disease. This knowledge was not available to doctors in the 17th century.

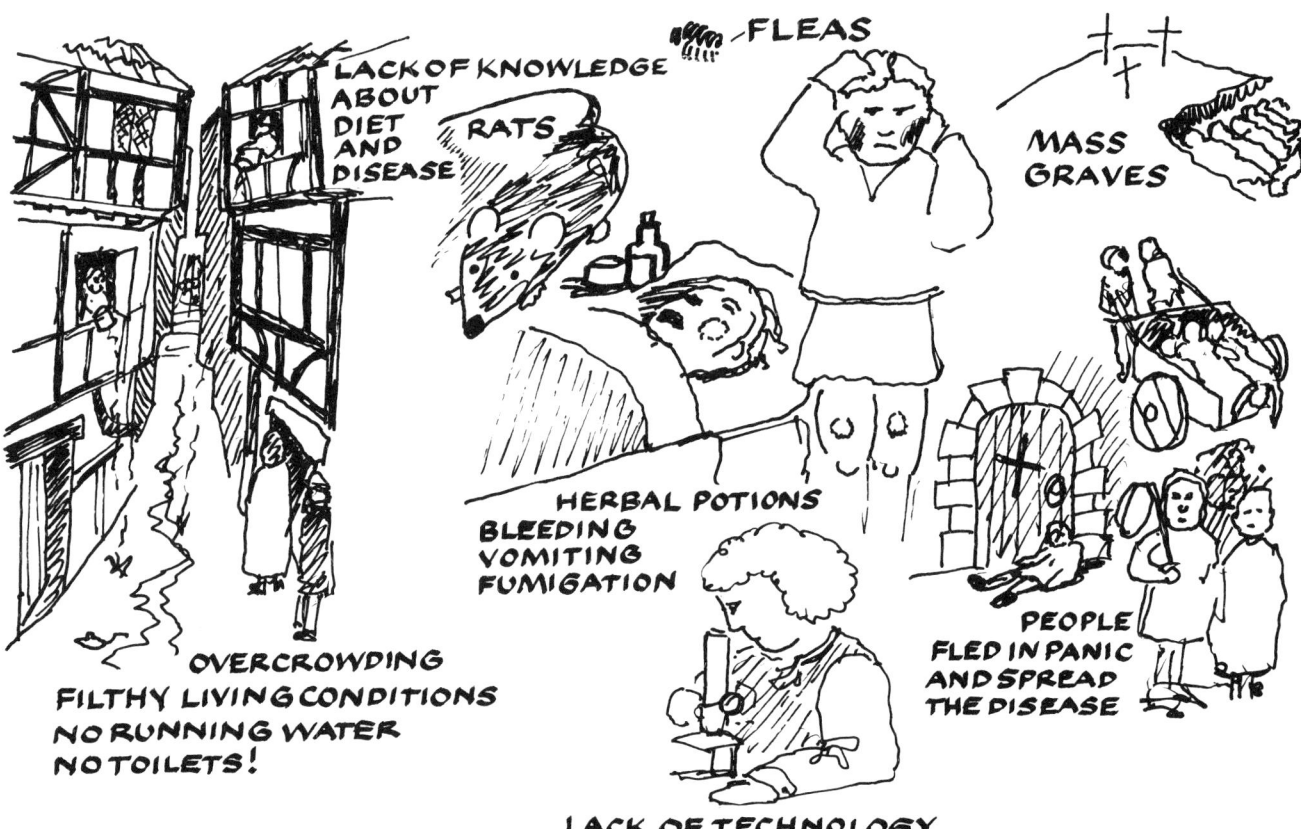

1 Design a poster that shows the main causes of the Plague.

2 Use the information in the diagram to write about causes, symptoms, treatment and results of the Plague.

3 Work out the diseases, which have been jumbled up.

    IDHPYTO   LMAESES   RCECNA

        RHCLEOA   LXOPLAMS

A LITTLE KNOWLEDGE IS A DANGEROUS THING!

Between the 15th and 18th centuries a knowledge of countryside remedies could get people into trouble, especially those who knew about the use of wild plants and herbs for medicines. They could be accused of WITCHCRAFT. It was an age when scientific knowledge was limited, and people believed in witches, warlocks and wizards and their ability to make potions and cast spells. It was a way of explaining the inexplicable! The trouble was that many innocent people died as a result of this belief.

1. Can you find the following words in the word search: TANSY, BETONY, MINT, SAGE, FEVERFEW, NETTLES, PARSLEY, ROSEMARY, ROSE, YARROW, VIOLET, FENNEL, FOXGLOVE, CHIVE, WOAD, THYME.

2. Find out about the work of the following people:
   NICHOLAS CULPEPER (HERBALIST), MATTHEW HOPKINS (WITCHFINDER GENERAL)

3. Write a story explaining how an old woman living alone in a 16th century town might be accused of witchcraft. You will need to look up information about the treatment of witches.

How my Lord and Lady dress

Trace the figures onto card (or you can stick them onto card). Then colour them and cut them out.

Now make a stage for your figures. You will need another piece of card about the size of this page. Make a fold along the side about 6cm from the edge. Colour the base to look like a road. Draw and colour a scene above the road. You could make it a country scene with a Georgian mansion in the park or it could be a town scene. Either way you will have to look up the type of architecture in a reference book.

Now position your figures and stick them onto your stage (you will need to find a way to support the back).

Finally, make a stand-up card, and on it write a description of the costume figures.

THESE WORDS MIGHT HELP

HIS
Three-cornered hat
Embroidered waistcoat
Fine silk stockings
Large cuffs fitted to the wrist
Powdered wig and sidecurls

HERS
Embroidered fabric
Lace frills
Wide panniers
Tiny cap on powdered wig

ROLL ON

In the 18th century, improvements in transport were necessary because of the growing population and the need to move raw materials to the new factories.

Roads were improved by men such as **METCALF, TELFORD** and **BRINDLEY**. The new **TURNPIKE** roads had hard surfaces so traffic was not slowed down by ruts or holes. Journeys were speeded up and were more comfortable but there was a price to pay: tolls were charged. Metcalf was an amazing man – he was blind. Telford and Brindley also built canals which were useful in moving large, heavy goods or fragile things. **BARGES** were pulled by horses. **CANALS** had to be kept level so **LOCKS** or **TUNNELS** were used to solve the problem of hills.

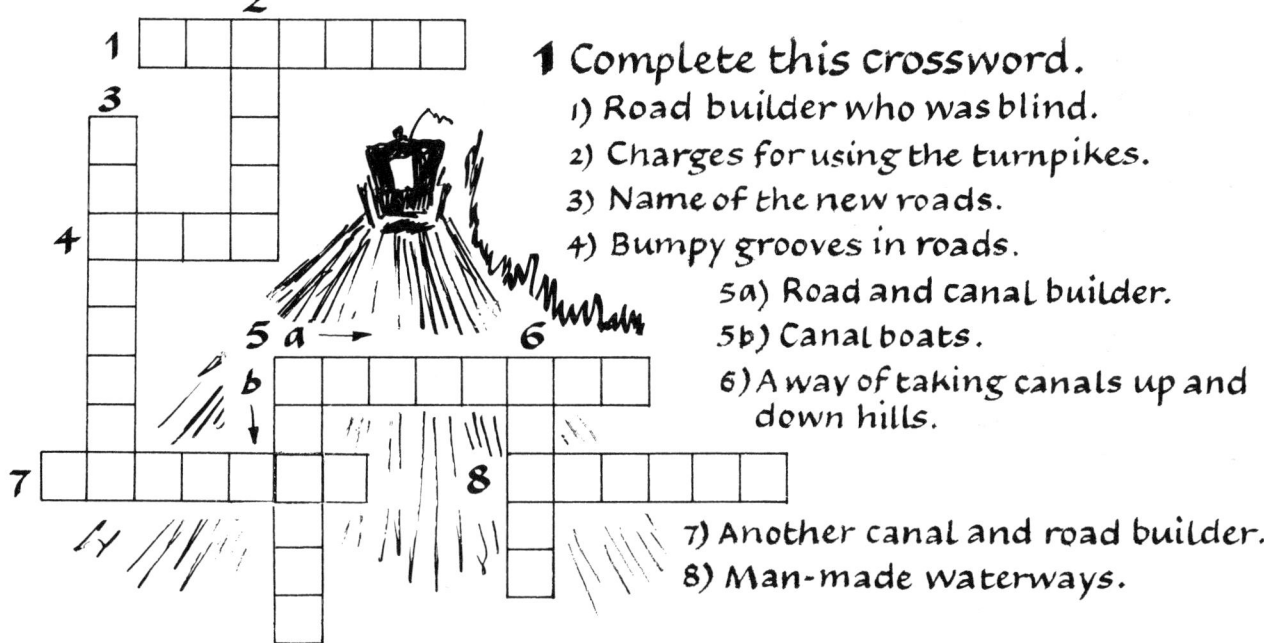

1 Complete this crossword.
- 1) Road builder who was blind.
- 2) Charges for using the turnpikes.
- 3) Name of the new roads.
- 4) Bumpy grooves in roads.
- 5a) Road and canal builder.
- 5b) Canal boats.
- 6) A way of taking canals up and down hills.
- 7) Another canal and road builder.
- 8) Man-made waterways.

USE YOUR REFERENCE OR LIBRARY BOOKS TO ANSWER THESE QUESTIONS

2 Find out more about Metcalf and Brindley.

3 Find out how much people had to pay to use the new roads.

HIGHWAY

Travelling by road in the 18th century was very often slow, difficult and dangerous. This was due to the terrible conditions of the roads which were, in many places, nothing more than tracks.

Using dice and counters, play this game and find out for yourself some of the problems facing 18th century travellers.

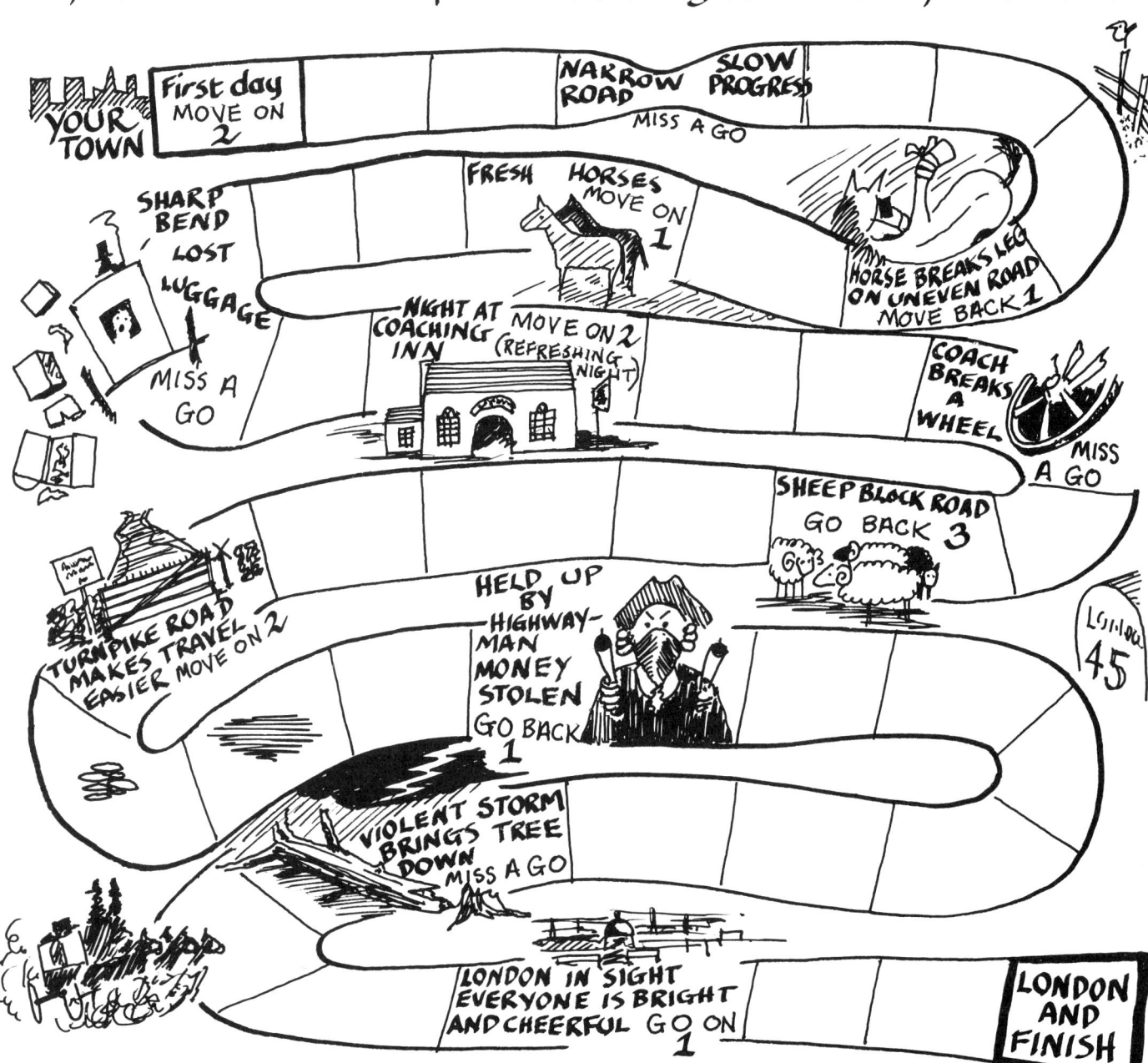

1. Using the information found in the game, write a story describing a journey along an 18th century road.
2. Invent your own board game based upon today's roads.
3. Find out more about highwaymen such as DICK TURPIN.

DOWN ON THE FARM

During the 18th century there was a major change in the way people in England farmed. No longer were fields divided into strips to be worked by individuals. Now land was enclosed and large fields appeared. This major change or revolution in farming allowed men such as **JETHRO TULL**, **LORD TOWNSHEND**, **THOMAS COKE** and **ROBERT BAKEWELL** to bring about an improvement in the quality of crops and animals.

In the wordsearch below there are 25 words about farming and 18th century farmers. How many can you find?

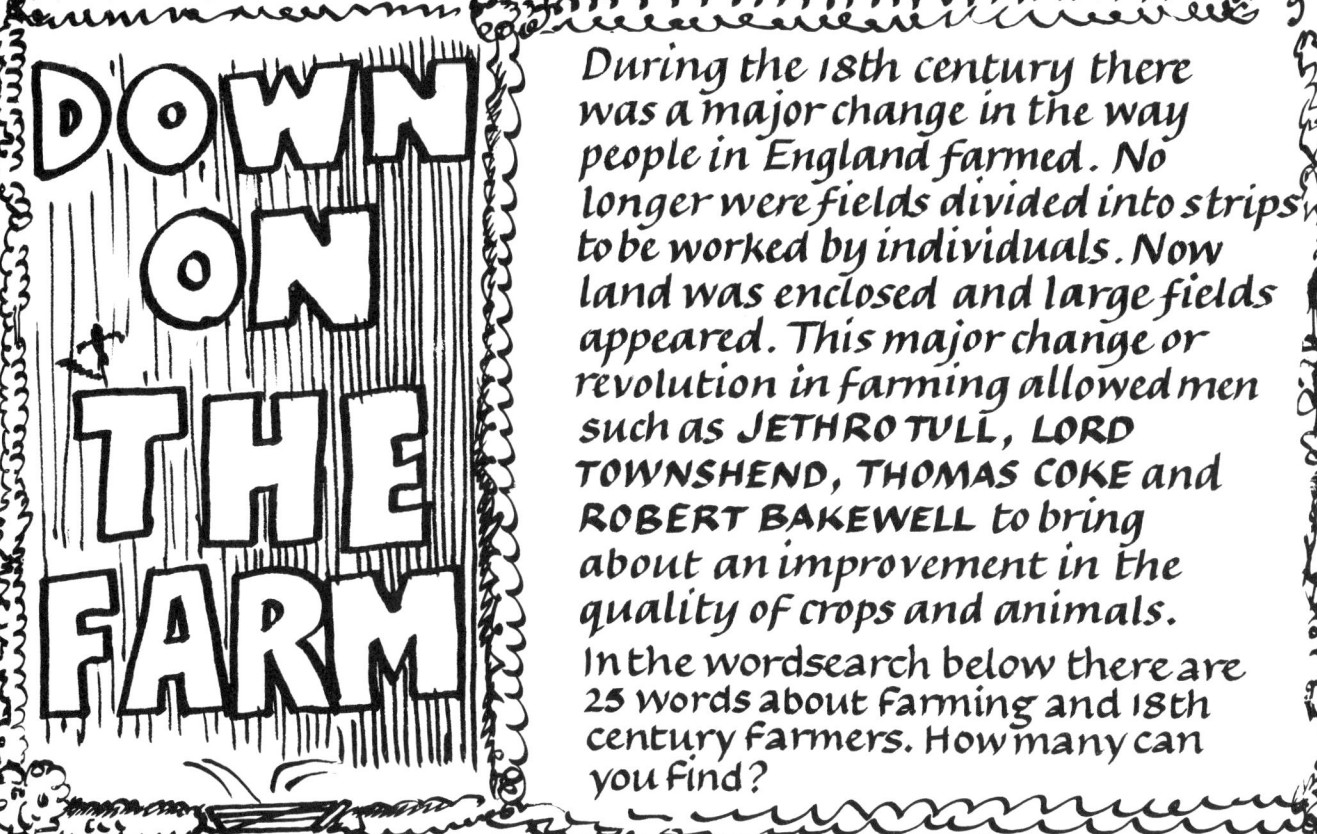

Find out the names of the jumbled up animals:
- GPI
- RHSOE
- EKIHCCN
- OWC
- OEGHEPDS
- ERHIFE
- OPNY
- IKLUGDCN
- VEOD
- BIARBT

© Collins Educational — Handy ideas for Hassled History Teachers — You may photocopy this page for use in the classroom

BLACK GOLD

Coal has always been a useful fossil fuel but it was not until the invention of the steam engine that coal became really important. During the 19th century, mining for coal was often a hard and dangerous job, and frequent accidents and disasters claimed the lives of many men, women and children.

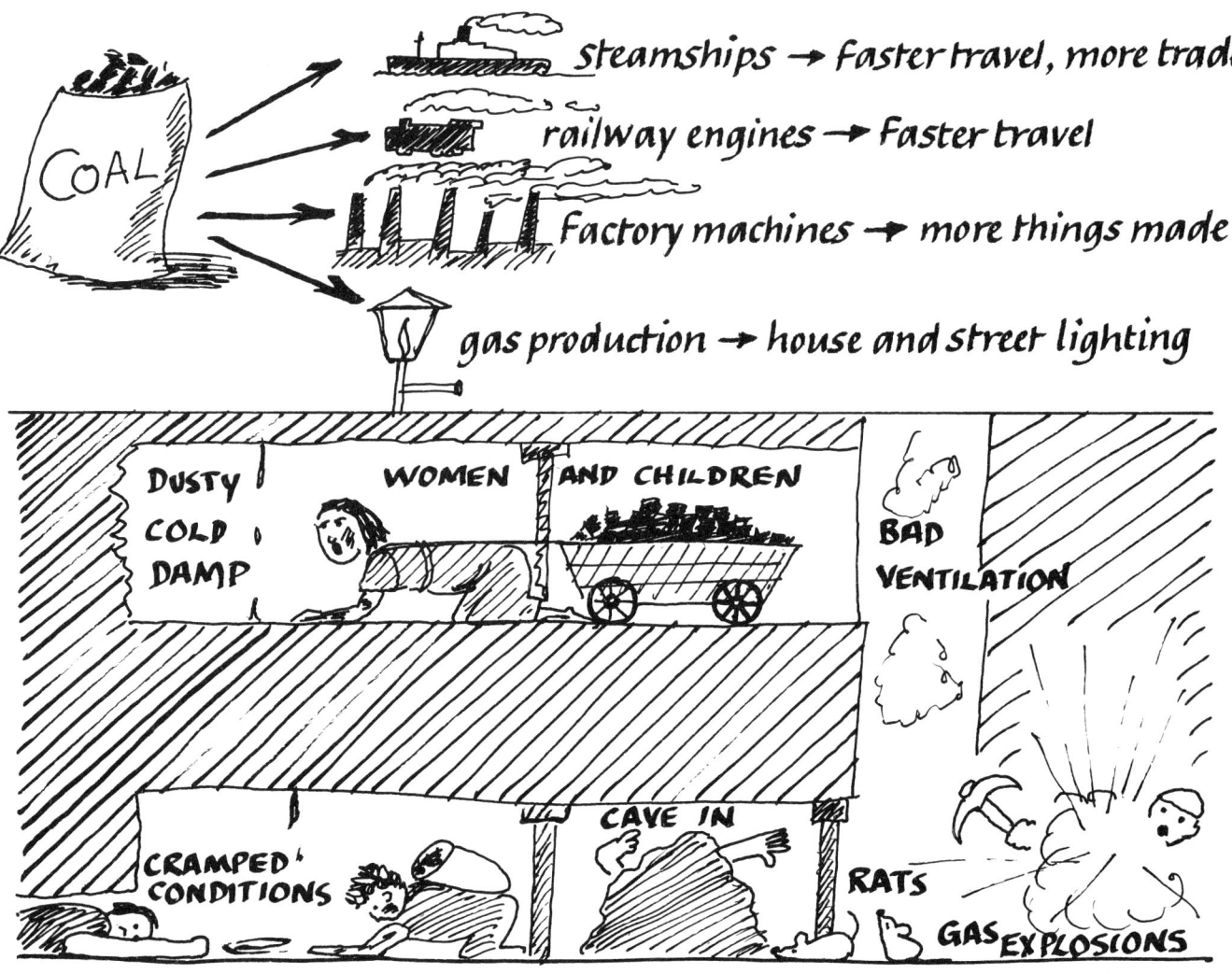

1. In your own words explain why coal was so important in the 19th century.
2. What were the dangers faced by miners in the 19th century?
3. Do you think it was right or wrong for women and children to work underground in mines? Talk about this with others and then write about the good and bad points.
4. Use your ideas to hold a class discussion. Take a vote to see who is for or against.

OUTLINE MAP OF THE BRITISH ISLES

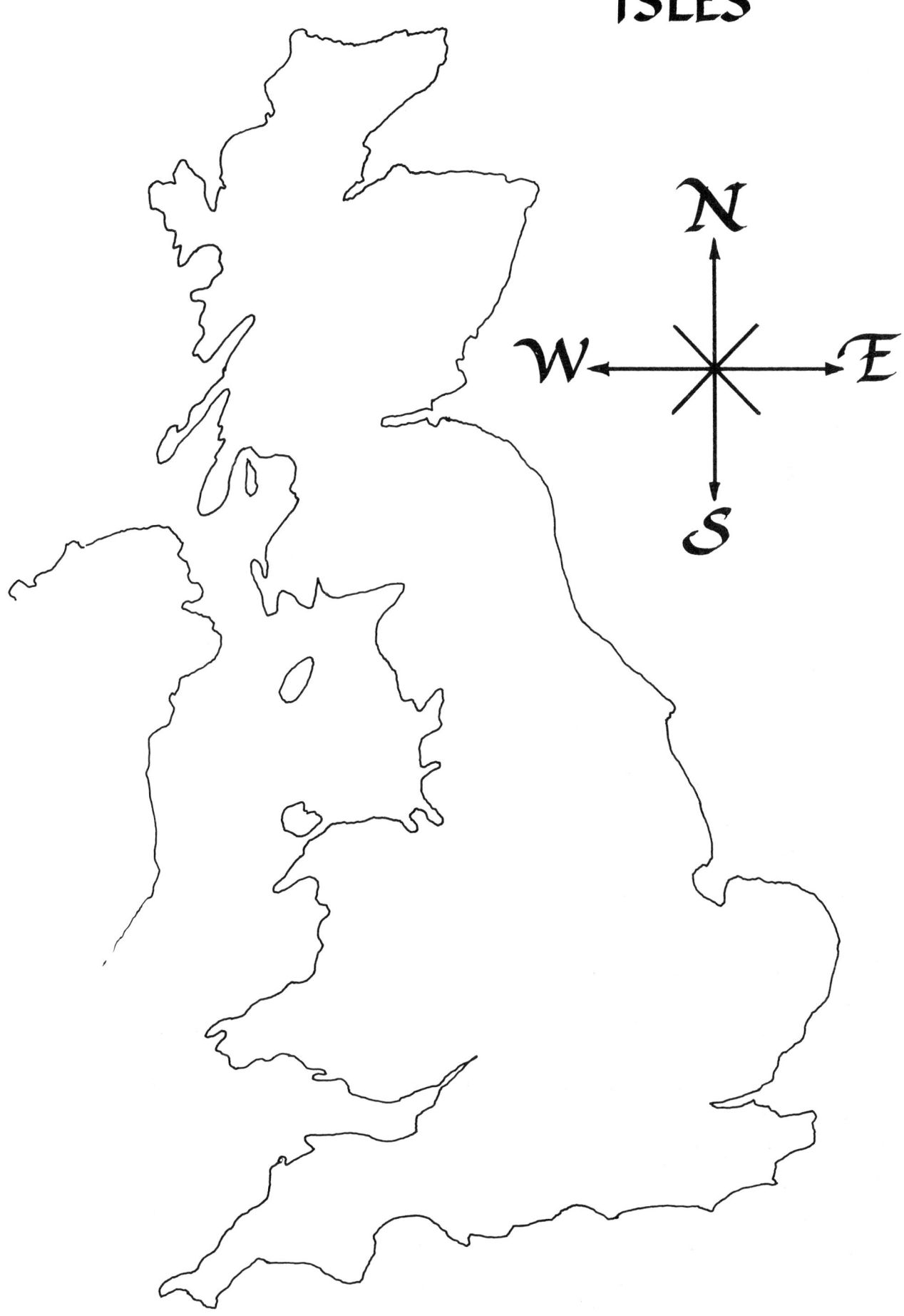